Start Up Science 4

GODFREY HALL

Illustrated by Beverley Sprio

© 2000 Times Media Private Limited

EARLYBIRD BOOKS
An imprint of Times Media Private Limited
A member of the Times Publishing Group
Times Centre, 1 New Industrial Road, Singapore 536196
E-mail: fps@tpl.com.sg
Online Book Store: http://www.timesone.com.sg/fpl

First published 1997
Reprinted 1998, 2000, 2001

ISBN 981 01 0663 7

Printed by Stamford Press Pte Ltd, Singapore

D1299709

earlybird books

CONTENTS

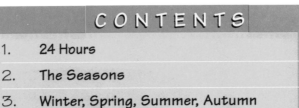

1. 24 HOURS

It takes the earth 24 hours or one day and one night to spin round once. As the earth spins, part of it faces the sun and part of it is in the dark. It is daytime in the parts of the earth facing the sun. It is night-time in the parts of the earth facing away from the sun.

Circle the things in the Night drawing that are different from the drawing of Day.

Day

Night

2. THE SEASONS

In some countries, there are four seasons in a year. The seasons are winter, spring, summer and autumn.

Look at the pictures and read what happens during each season. Now colour the pictures.

In the winter, it gets colder. In some parts of the world, it even snows.

In spring, the flowers begin to grow. Blossoms can be found on the trees. Many animals have babies in this season.

In summer, lots of people go on holiday. The days are long and often warm and sunny.

In autumn, animals begin to get ready for winter. Birds fly off to warmer countries and the leaves fall off some of the trees.

In different parts of the world, there are often special days and events taking place in each season. Here are some of the events that take place in different countries around the world.

Mid Summer's Day. Sweden, Finland. Summer. People have parties and build bonfires to celebrate the middle of summer.

Halloween. USA and England. Autumn. Children dress up as witches and ghosts.

Christmas Day. All over the world. Winter in some countries, summer in others. People celebrate the birth of Jesus Christ and children look forward to getting gifts from Santa Claus.

Holi. India and Asia. Spring. This is celebrated with street dancing, processions and bonfires.

Look at the pictures and complete these sentences.

1.

There are no _____ on many of the trees in winter.

2.

In _____ many of the trees begin to grow leaves again.

3.

In summer, the _____ are covered in leaves.

4.

In autumn, many of the trees lose their leaves ready for _____.

5

A great deal of the earth is covered by sea. The rest of the earth is covered by land. There are forests, mountains, lakes and rivers on the land. There are coral reefs and many plants and animals in the sea. Many of the oceans and seas are very deep.

Look at these pictures below. Write 'l' by the things or animals you can find on land and 's' by those you can find in the sea.

1. desert _____

2. submarine _____

3. parrot _____

4. mountains _____

5. whale _____

6. large ship _____

7. giraffe _____

8. paddy field _____

5. THE EARTH AT WORK

The Earth is always changing. When the Earth moves, there may be earthquakes. Sometimes, volcanoes erupt, throwing out hot rocks. The weather changes all the time as well. Sometimes, it is vey hot and dry and sometimes, heavy monsoon rains fall and terrible winds like typhoons cause floods.

Each sentence below describes one of the pictures shown. Write the number of the sentence below the picture it describes.

A. (　)

B. (　)

C. (　)

D. (　)

1. Earthquakes shake the ground. Houses fall down and many people can get killed.

2. During a typhoon, there can be strong winds, heavy rains and huge waves.

3. Monsoon rains are often very heavy and can cause terrible floods.

4. Volcanoes explode and hot rocks and lava pour out.

A **volcano** is a mountain with a hole in it. When a **volcano** erupts, it throws out hot rock and ash. About 25 **volcanoes** erupt every year. The hot rock is called lava. It is so hot that it can flow along the ground like oil. The ash from the **volcano** is good for growing things. This is what the inside of a **volcano** looks like.

Circle the correct word in each of these sentences.

1. Lava is (hot, cold, warm) liquid rock.

2. About (25, 300, 100) volcanoes erupt each year.

3. Lava is very (good, dangerous, cold).

4. The ash from a (volcano, fire, car) is thrown high into the air.

5. The ash is (good, bad, too large) for growing things.

Etna, Mayon, Gunung Agung and Mauna Loa are names of four volcanoes. Can you find them on a map?

7. TROUBLE ON THE PLANET

It is important that we look after our planet. It is our home. We have to try and keep it clean. We must keep seas and rivers clean by not throwing too much rubbish in them. We should not use too many cars and lorries on the road because these vehicles make the air dirty. We must not chop down too many trees or kill too many animals.

Put a tick beside the things we are doing right and a cross beside the things we are doing wrong.

1. Throwing rubbish in rivers. ☐

2. Using fewer cars, lorries and buses. ☐

3. Taking too many fish from the sea. ☐

4. Chopping down rain forests. ☐

5. Using wind to make electricity. ☐

6. Destroying animals' homes. ☐

Write down three things that you think might happen to this lake if we started throwing a lot of rubbish and dirty water into it.

1. _____ .

2. _____ .

3. _____ .

8. CARING FOR OUR WORLD

We can do our bit to help care for our world. We can help save water and electricity in our homes every day. Instead of throwing containers away after using them, we can use them for storing things. In this way, we can help save the earth.

Look at this list. What can you do to help? Tick the ones you can help with.

1. Save paper and cards. Re-use them. ☐

2. Don't throw your rubbish into rivers and ponds. ☐

3. Don't pick wild flowers. ☐

4. Cut down on bags, use your own shopping basket. ☐

5. Don't use too much water. ☐

How are these children helping?

A.

_____

_____

_____

B.

_____

_____

_____

C.

_____

_____

_____

9. THE SOLAR SYSTEM

The earth moves around the sun. It takes one year for the earth to travel round once. Besides the earth, other planets also move round the sun. The sun, earth and other planets make up the **solar system**.

Fill in the blanks with the correct names of the planets in our solar system. Use the words in the box to help you.

A. M_ _ _ _ _ _

B. V_ _ _ _

C. E_ _ _ _

D. M_ _ _

E. J_ _ _ _ _ _ _

F. S_ _ _ _ _

G. U_ _ _ _ _

H. N_ _ _ _ _ _

I. P_ _ _ _

✎ Pluto ✎ Uranus ✎ Jupiter ✎ Mercury ✎ Mars
✎ Venus ✎ Earth ✎ Saturn ✎ Neptune

Which is the nearest to the sun? _____

Which is the furthest away? _____

Unscramble these names.

A. MRSA _____

B. NVEUS _____

C. LTPUO _____

D. ARTEH _____

10. The Inner Planets

Mercury, Venus, Earth and Mars are called the Inner Planets because they are closest to the sun.

Mercury is the nearest planet to the sun. One side is very hot, one side is very cold. It is a small planet.

Venus is covered by clouds. It is very hot. It is the brightest planet in the night sky.

Mars is called the 'Red' planet. It is very cold. It is a lot smaller than the Earth.

Earth is our home planet. It is covered by land and sea. The Earth is just the right distance from the sun for us to live on it.

Write one sentence about each of these planets.

Earth _____

Venus _____

Mercury _____

Mars _____

11. THE OUTER PLANETS

Jupiter, Saturn, Uranus, Neptune and Pluto are called the Outer Planets because they are further from the sun. Pluto is the smallest planet in the solar system. Jupiter is the largest. The Outer Planets are all very cold places. Pluto is the coldest. Saturn looks different from all the other planets because it has rings around it.

Circle the correct answers.

1. Uranus is one of the (**Inner, Outer, Middle**) Planets.

2. Jupiter is the (**biggest, smallest, warmest**) planet in the solar system.

3. Neptune is a very (**hot, cold, sunny**) planet.

4. (**Pluto, Jupiter, Saturn**) looks different from the other planets because it has rings around it.

5. Pluto is the (**hottest, biggest, coldest**) planet in the solar system.

12. THE MOON

You have learnt that the earth spins round once every day. The moon spins round once every 27 days. It goes round the earth once a month. There is no air on the moon. Nothing lives on it. It is full of very large holes called **craters**.

Here is one way of making your own craters.

1. Put a tray of sand or flour on the floor.
2. Drop some marbles or small stones onto the tray.
3. Lift them carefully off the tray.
4. The holes that are left are your craters.

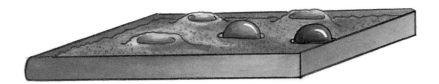

Put a tick beside the correct statements and a cross beside the wrong statements.

1. The moon spins round once every day. ☐

2. There is a lot of air on the moon. ☐

3. Astronauts have landed on the moon. ☐

4. There are many plants and animals on the moon. ☐

5. The moon is full of craters. ☐

13. THE SUN

The Sun is a star. It is a ball of very hot gas. Without the sun, there would be no animals or plants on earth. The sun is a lot bigger than the earth. It is a very long way from the earth and it is very, very hot. The earth goes round the sun. **Never** look at the sun as it can damage your eyes.

Circle the words to do with the sun.

hot   star   life

door   carpet   light   cold

plants   animals   doctor

run   cup

Draw a sunrise or sunset below.

14. COMETS

Comets are like very large and dirty snowballs. They travel round the sun and solar system. The most famous comet takes 76 years to travel round the sun. It is called Halley's Comet. It was last seen in 1986. Comets have huge tails made of gas and dust.

Unscramble these words.

A. METCO — _____

B. NUS — _____

C. TSDU — _____

D. LLEHAY'S — _____

E. SAG — _____

Use the words above to fill in the blanks below.

1. A _____ is like a dirty snowball.

2. Never look at the _____ because it can damage your eyes.

3. Comet tails are made of _____ and gas.

4. _____ Comet was last seen in 1986.

5. When you look at a comet, some of what you see is _____.

Look up into the night sky and you will see thousands of stars. Each one of these stars is a sun. They are hot balls of gas which seem to twinkle. They are very far away from the earth. Many years ago, sailors used the position of the stars in the sky to help them find their way.

Colour in the picture of the night sky.

It would take us thousands of years to reach the nearest star. Our solar system is part of a huge group of stars called the Milky Way.

The earth is in one of the arms. The shape of the Milky Way is changing all the time.

Circle the letters that make up the words 'Milky Way'.

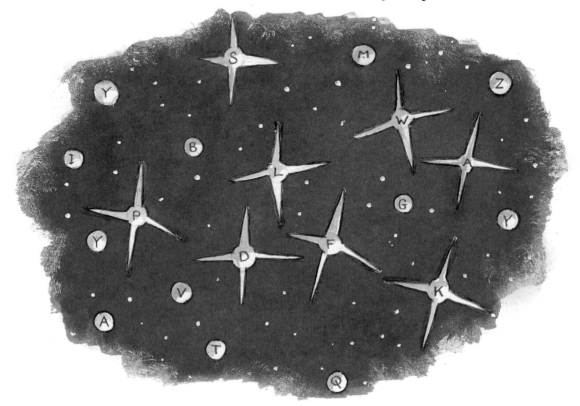

17. SPACE VEHICLES

Lots of special vehicles are used in space. Some of them have men or women in them. Others do not. Many of these travel millions of miles to other planets.

A **rocket** is a powerful flying machine that is able to travel in space.

A **satellite** goes round the earth or another planet and sends back information.

A **space shuttle** travels to and from space.

A **space station** orbits the earth and sends back information. A number of astronauts live inside it.

A **lunar buggy** is used on the moon for travelling about.

The names of the vehicles drawn in the left column are written in the right column but not in the correct order. Join each vehicle to its name.

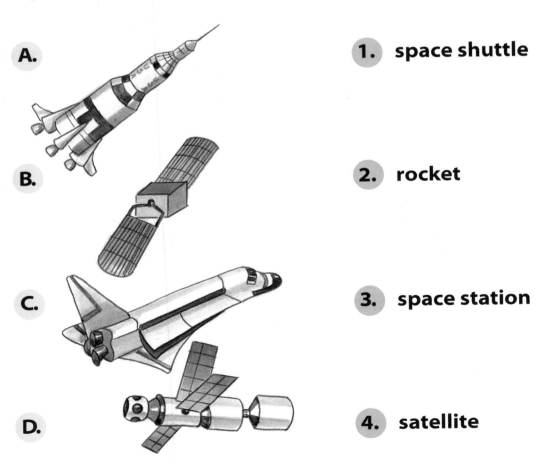

A.

B.

C.

D.

1. **space shuttle**

2. **rocket**

3. **space station**

4. **satellite**

A rocket is used to get into space. It needs a great deal of energy to leave the earth. As a rocket climbs through the sky, parts of it are used up and fall off. It gets lighter as it gets higher until it goes into outer space.

Here is a simple way of making your own rocket engine.

You will need:
a sausage-shaped balloon
a bulldog clip
two chairs
straws
cord
tape

1. Blow up the balloon. Fix the clip onto the end.

2. Stick the straw on the top of the balloon.

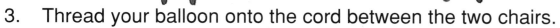

3. Thread your balloon onto the cord between the two chairs.
4. Take off the clip and watch your rocket go!

Draw in the rest of the rocket below the nose cone.

19. THE SPACE SHUTTLE

The space shuttle is a rocket that can be used over and over again in space. It is sent into space using a huge tank of fuel. This then drops off. The space shuttle returns to earth by gliding back.

Colour in the drawing below.

The first satellite was launched in 1957. Since then, over 2,000 satellites have been sent into space. Some satellites are used to take pictures of the weather on earth, others are used to send television pictures or messages around the world.

You have been sent into space to bring back as many satellites as you can find. Throw a six to start. See how many satellites you can collect before reaching the finish. The winner is the one with the largest number. To collect a satellite, you must land on a satellite square.

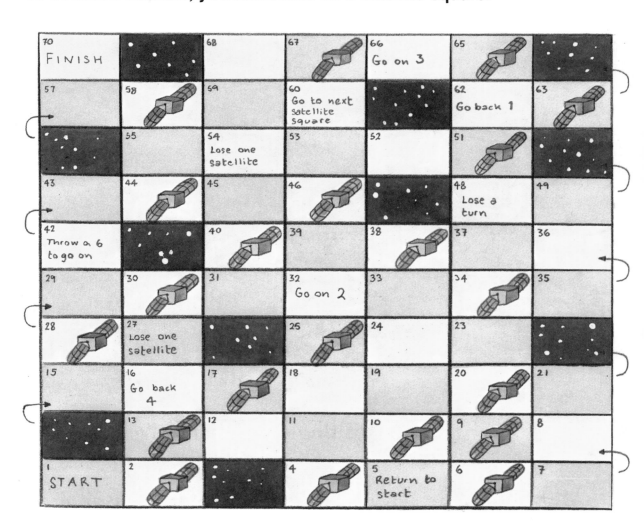

Scientists believe that there could be life in outer space. Using telescopes, space rockets and satellites, they have studied many of the planets and stars. They have sent messages into space and put them on board rockets which have travelled to planets and far out into the solar system.

If there is anyone out there, how might they send messages to us? Circle the possible answers.

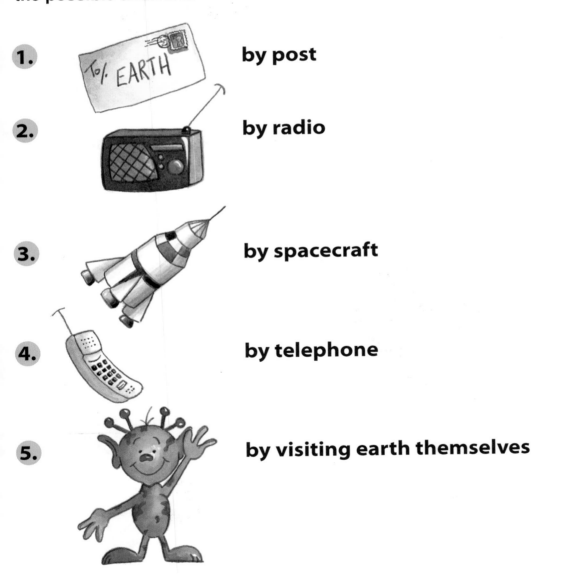

1. by post

2. by radio

3. by spacecraft

4. by telephone

5. by visiting earth themselves

Astronomers have been looking at the stars for thousands of years. Ancient people looked at the stars to decide when to plant their crops. They also observed the stars when making stone circles. They used these stone circles as calendars. Telescopes are used to look at the stars.

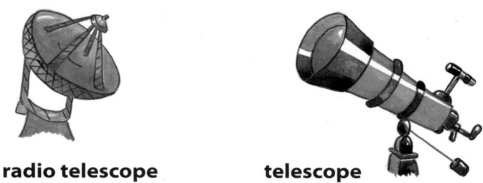

radio telescope   **telescope**

Galilei Galileo was the first person to use a telescope to look at the stars nearly 400 years ago.

Circle which of these you could use to look at the stars.

binoculars   **cup**

radio telescope   **book**

eye   **telescope**

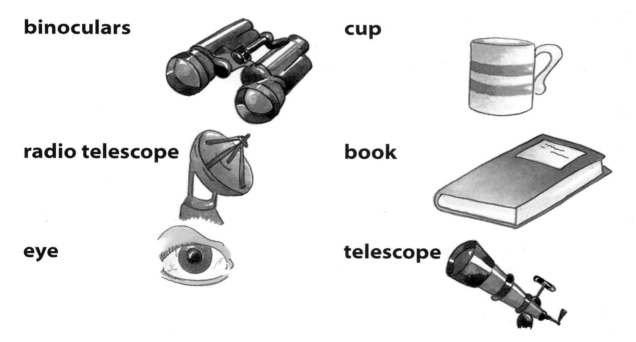

24

23. Pictures In The Sky

When you look up at the stars, they all look muddled up. But if you look carefully, you may see that they form some patterns. These patterns are called **constellations**.

Join up the dots below to make some of these patterns.

1. The Plough

2. Pavo*

3. Orion*

4. Scutum*

5. Libra*

6. Southern Cross

* Seen in the Southern Hemisphere.

Meteors can sometimes be seen in the sky. They are tiny pieces of rock which burn into nothing as they enter the earth's atmosphere. Meteors are also called **shooting stars**. **Meteorites** are much bigger and can make large holes called craters when they hit the ground.

Circle the correct answers to these questions.

1. The hole made by a meteorite is called a (**star** / **crater**).

2. Can meteors be seen in the sky? (**yes** / **no**)

3. What is another name for a meteor? (**shooting star** / **comet**)

4. What happens when meteors get into the atmosphere?
(**they burn up** / **they get bigger**)

5. Which is bigger, a meteor or a meteorite? (**meteor** / **meteorite**)

6. Meteors are tiny pieces of (**ice** / **rock**).

Animals, insects and plants often live together in **communities**. If you look carefully at a tree, you may see birds living in the branches, insects in the bark and plants underneath it. A pond can have frogs, lilies and fish living in and around it.

Look at the creatures. Where does each creature live? Join each creature with the community where it lives.

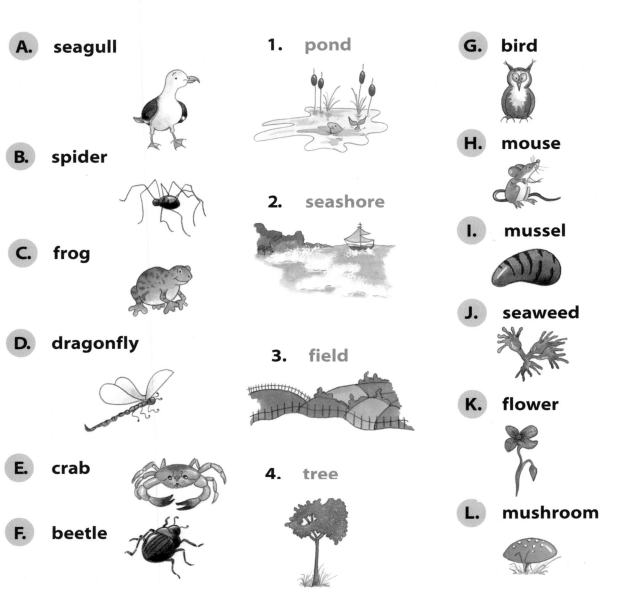

A. seagull

B. spider

C. frog

D. dragonfly

E. crab

F. beetle

1. pond

2. seashore

3. field

4. tree

G. bird

H. mouse

I. mussel

J. seaweed

K. flower

L. mushroom

Certain places have many different plants and animals living in it because there is plenty of food and water to be found and because the weather is not too hot or too cold. Not many plants and animals live in a desert, where it is very hot and dry or at the North Pole where it is very cold all year round.

Look at the creatures below and join each one with the best place for it to live.

1. seagull

A. bushes

2. spider

B. grasslands and plains

3. worm

C. compost heap

4. lion

D. seashore

27. FOODCHAINS

Animals need food to live. They eat either plants or other animals. Some animals eat both plants and other animals. Plants do not need to eat. They store energy that they produce when the sun shines. When an animal eats a plant and is eaten by another animal, a **food chain** is formed.

The drawings show food chains of plants and animals. Some animals have been left out. See if you can write the names of the correct animals.

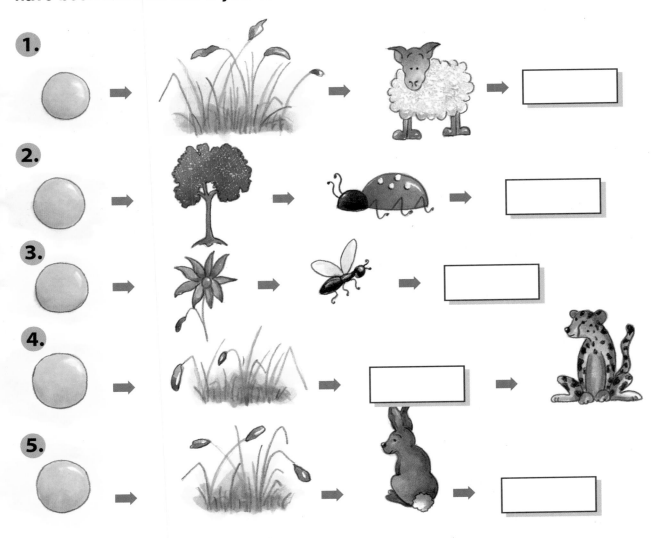

✎ **bird** ✎ **spider** ✎ **fox** ✎ **deer** ✎ **human**

It is important that animals and plants have the right food to eat and a suitable place to live. Sometimes, disease or predators may destroy them. Often, our activities may harm the environment they live in.

Look at what is happening in these drawings. Write down beside each drawing why these activities may upset where plants and animals live.

1.

_____
_____
_____
_____
_____
_____

2.

_____
_____
_____
_____
_____
_____

3.

_____
_____
_____
_____
_____
_____

Not all plants and animals can live in the same place. Some need somewhere warm and wet. Some need a place which is cold and dry.

**Some of these animals belong in a forest community. Others do not.
Circle the creatures and plants that you think do not belong here.**

ANSWERS

Chapter 3.	1. leaves, 2. spring, 3. trees, 4. winter.
Chapter 4.	1. l, 2. s, 3. l, 4. l, 5. s, 6. l, (rivers or lakes) or s, 7. l, 8. l.
Chapter 5.	A. 3, B. 1, C. 4, D. 2.
Chapter 6.	1. hot, 2. 25, 3. dangerous, 4. volcano, 5. good.
Chapter 7.	Tick – 2, 5; Cross – 1, 3, 4, 6. 1. The fish and other animals will die. 2. The plants will die. 3. The children will not be able to swim in the lake any more.
Chapter 8.	1. They are walking to school instead of going by car. Too many cars can make the air dirty. 2. They are saving paper by recycling the newspapers and cards instead of throwing them away. 3. They are recycling the ice-cream boxes instead of throwing them away.
Chapter 9.	A. Mercury, B. Venus, C. Earth, D. Mars, E. Jupiter, F. Saturn, G. Uranus, H.Neptune, I. Pluto; Mercury Pluto; A. Mars, B. Venus, C. Pluto, D. Earth.
Chapter 11.	1. Outer, 2. biggest, 3. cold, 4. Saturn, 5. coldest.

Chapter 12.	Tick – 3,5; cross 1,2,4.
Chapter 13.	hot, star, life, light, cold, plants, animals.
Chapter 14.	A. comet, B. sun, C. dust, D. Halley's, D.gas.
Chapter 17.	A2, B4, C1, D3.
Chapter 21.	2, 3, 5.
Chapter 22.	binoculars, eye, telescope.
Chapter 24.	1. crater, 2. yes, 3. shooting star, 4. they burn up, 5. meteorite, 6. rock.
Chapter 25.	1. C, D; 2. A, E, I, J; 3. H, K, L; 4. B, F, G, L.
Chapter 26.	1D, 2A, 3C, 4B.
Chapter 27.	1. human, 2. bird, 3. spider, 4. deer, 5. fox.